KNEE ABILITY ZERO

Ben Patrick

TABLE OF CONTENTS

HERE'S WHY ZERO IS A SLAM DUNK

The book you hold in your hands is one of the key discoveries in modern training.

The cost of damaged human bodies goes way beyond the mountains of dollars invested in medications, treatment, lost productivity, joint replacements and disability services. As we bring new health and ability into the body, we reinvigorate our humanity.

"Check out @kneesovertoesguy" ... That was the first I heard of the author Ben Patrick. This Instagram tip started a chain reaction that changed my path in life and is changing the way the world trains.

When I looked at Ben's page in late 2018, he had 5k followers and a cool gym in Florida. I dropped him a DM to say I appreciated his work, and a friendship began.

I later found out that Ben had seen some of my original YouTube videos from back in 2012 when I was first deep squatting and sharing lessons from our common mentor, strength legend Charles Poliquin.

As I studied Ben's system, I realized that he had cracked the code I'd been looking for: A method for training away joint and tendon pain and replacing it with elite athletic ability.

ZERO was a solution by necessity in 2020 when millions lost their gym access but didn't want to lose their gains. ZERO has now become much more than an alternative while gyms are closed. It's a fully scalable program you can do anytime, anywhere to build athleticism and decrease injury.

As you're about to experience, strength training without weights leaves you feeling strong and energized - ready for whatever life throws at you. But don't take my word for it. Listen to the thousands of stories from real people who are back doing what they love thanks to ATG. Then try it for yourself.

Beyond his physical transformation from athletic basket-case to dunking dreams, Ben Patrick's relentless enthusiasm and positivity are no doubt part of the ZERO special sauce.

Now it's your turn to feel the energy of ZERO and share the results with those you love.

- Keegan Smith

IN THE BEGINNING

I can still remember being 4 years old and telling my best friend I was going to save up for a Michael Jordan rookie card. I worked odd jobs, saved every penny, and at age 6 I did it: I bought a Michael Jordan rookie card for one thousand dollars. I had no interest in toys: just Jordan.

First thing after waking up each day, I raced to the couch to turn on the TV, but not to watch cartoons...

(From the 1990 video "NBA Superstars")

An F-16 Fighting Falcon appears on the screen.

Michael Jordan enters the tunnel into the arena.

The F-16 approaches the runway, then Jordan steps onto the court.

The F-16 begins accelerating for takeoff, and Jordan begins dribbling down the court.

The F-16 gets faster. Jordan gets faster! F-16 - Jordan! Back and forth they go, 'til the F-16 lifts off and Jordan soars into the air for a dunk!

Berlin's "Take My Breath Away" begins to play, and slow motion highlights of Michael Jordan ensue.

Many hours a day I practiced these dunks on my Little Tike hoop in the garage. By age 9 I was waking up at 5 a.m. to do vertical jump programs before school. Thousands of nights I dreamed of dunking like Michael Jordan. Not once did I dream of lying half-naked on an operating table as doctors used markers to draw where they were going to cut me open.

Chronic knee pain secretly dominated my life starting at age 12. I remember during a fire drill at school being worried that if a real fire erupted, I'd be the last one out. Unless I was warmed up I couldn't even run, and I had to go up and down stairs very slowly to avoid the pain.

By 14 it was not so secret: My teammates and coaches nicknamed me "Old Man" because my knees were so stiff. I finished high school with scars on my knee, not even close to dunking a basketball, and with no college coaches interested in giving me a scholarship.

I recall the moment it hit home that my dream of being a basketball player had not succeeded. I had a real decision to make: What would I do with my life now? Would I choose a logical career and forget basketball, or would I devote my existence to figuring out how to bulletproof my knees?

I chose the latter. I began painting walls during the day to make money while I studied and experimented with how to fix my knees.

A year went by with no results. In fact, I was certain I needed another surgery when a spark of truth finally presented itself...

"The athlete whose knees can go farthest and strongest over his or her toes is the most protected."

Everything I had been taught up to that point by dozens of trainers and physical therapists was very clear: NO KNEES OVER TOES - but when I read this statement, I immediately knew it was true.

I scrambled on the internet looking for examples of this truth, and the first video footage I found was from Australian Strength Coach Keegan Smith, a student of Charles Poliquin. I became a student of Charles myself, and learned enough to get my knees to the point where I could play basketball with manageable pain.

At age 21, I beat the odds and signed a college basketball scholarship with an up-and-coming coach named Jeremy Shulman. He was the only coach who gave me a shot, and I repaid him by becoming the starting point guard for his team and helping him win two straight conference championships in one of the strongest community college divisions in the nation.

At age 23, I received a full-ride scholarship offer from Boston University. From unrecruited in high school to Division 1 scholarship, local kids back home were reaching out to have me train them whenever I was in town. No one had ever heard of such a story, and people wanted to know how I had pulled it off.

Little did I know, an NCAA rule allowed only 5 years of eligibility to play sports after graduating high school, and my time was up. I assembled all my medical records, and Boston University appealed the ruling, but once again I was denied. It was suggested that I get a lawyer and fight the decision in time for the start of the season, but I knew it was meant to be: My purpose was to follow the clues I learned from Charles Poliquin, and see what I could achieve with knees over toes.

Fast forward to today. At 30 years old I have the abilities I always dreamed of: I can DUNK, and not just a little bit. I've now trained many NBA players and it is still surreal for me, as a 6'1 guy who grew up unable to grab the rim, to teach 6'6"+ NBA players how to improve their dunks, and physically demonstrating the precise next dunk that will improve their game but which they cannot do yet, thanks to the system of knee training you are about to learn.

More importantly, the following formula puts the longevity of my knees in my hands, so now I'm looking forward to a very different future than my genetics and injury history indicated. My son turned 1 year old in September, and I've got a new dream: To still be able to dunk when he can dunk, too. Knee Ability gives me the tools to preserve my knees so I can be dunking in my 40s and help my son dunk despite genetics that wouldn't naturally get him there. The ultimate thrill is no longer dunking with studs, but having my son dunk with me.

And here's how that's going to happen.

KNEE ABILITY ZERO

Knee Ability Zero is a program which requires zero weights, zero equipment, and zero special abilities to start. You can read, study the pictures, and follow right along! I will teach you how to perform each exercise with written explanations and visual demonstrations. You will do the exercise, then come back to your book and read the "Why" behind the exercise.

OPTIONAL STEP 0: ROKP

ROKP is short for "Reverse Out Knee Pain." This is the loving term I've grown to use for the lowest level of knees over toes training: walking backward.

HOW

Walk backward for 10 minutes.

My mother, wife, baby, dog and I took to the park to find a safe, flat place to demonstrate this for you.

We each walked at our comfortable paces, and in all cases...

The knee goes over the toes!

These are live shots taken from naturally walking backward:

My mother, Celia: knee over toes!

My wife, Alissa: knee over toes!

Me (with Lucky guiding): knee over toes!

(In my case, you can see how wearing a barefoot-inspired shoe could even extend the benefits of ROKP to strengthen your feet! But special shoes are not required.)

If you or someone you're helping is particularly fragile, you can have one person stand to the side as a guide, walking forward:

For those with more intense knee demands, you can even add load to the motion. Surfaces and sleds vary in friction, but there is one factor I coach uniformly: your knee should be capable enough to still be over your toes on each step, without pain:

Pictured above is Derek Williams aka @mr1nf1n1ty. Derek reversed his athletic decline and achieved his most mobile body in his forties! I can personally attest that he has done over 100 miles of ROKP. I've done more ROKP with Derek than anyone else, so there's no one more suited for this section than him. Derek now makes innovative products which assist people with my programs.

Now consider that a sled costs a tiny fraction of the price of a new treadmill, *and* that you can use a treadmill itself for ROKP - BY TURNING IT OFF! Most treadmills will provide internal resistance. You can't adjust that resistance, so you may have to give yourself breaks during the 10 minutes if your muscles burn out.

WHY

In China, walking backward has been passed down from generation to generation for thousands of years as a method of preventing knee degeneration.

"A hundred steps backward are worth a thousand steps forward."

If you look at the angle of the knee when it goes over your toes, you can see how it relates to something like going down the stairs, which is one of the leading causes of death in elderly due to falling.

More recently, doctors have started using backward walking as an effective screening process for falling in elderly. That's fantastic! But the dots have not yet been connected in terms of making ROKP a uniformly scalable solution to help the rest of the population *before* knee problems develop.

And it's very clear to me that you don't need to do it forever. Thanks to the evolution of my program, I no longer need ROKP and I rarely ever do it. But I *did* do my 100 miles and I believe that assisted me in going from a fragile state to a far more bulletproof one:

10 minutes x 3 times per week x 2 years

That's a workable formula to patiently get it done.

Plus, I can now use 10 minutes as a pre-workout cardio routine *for* my knee longevity whenever I desire!

If you're in a more fragile state and you have the time and the means, I highly recommend ROKP as a wonderful tool to add to your routine before you go through the following 8 steps...

STEP 1: THE TIBIALIS RAISE

Your tibialis anterior muscle is on the front of your lower leg. It acts both to flex your toes up and to decelerate your foot when you walk, stop running, jump, etc., which you'll see examples of when you get to the "Why" section for this exercise:

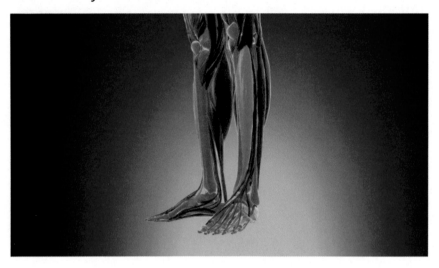

HOW

Find a wall and make sure you have safe footing (no socks or slippery floor).

Put your butt against the wall, and stand out a comfortable distance, with your legs straight:

Now, without letting your knees bend, flex your toes up and hold the top position for 2 seconds before lowering back down:

To make the exercise easier, simply stand closer to the wall:

To make the exercise harder, stand farther from the wall:

To help stabilize your learning process as you go through the book, my wife Alissa and I shot recap photos for each step, with her showing less difficulty and me showing more difficulty:

Perform 25 consecutive reps, pausing 2 seconds at the top of each rep and 2 seconds at the bottom of each rep, monitoring difficulty as you go. You may need to stand closer to the wall as your muscles burn out, or farther from the wall if you're feeling no challenge.

If you feel a significant burn by the end of the 25 reps, and no knee pain:

YOU JUST PUT MONEY IN THE BANK FOR YOUR BODY!

This is the beauty of Knee Ability: It's a program of pain-free ability, where our goal is never a win/lose situation, but rather degrees of winning only. Let's look at why that is...

WHY

You use your tibialis with every step you take:

When you play sports and decelerate or jump, you may put thousands of pounds of force into this muscle, and whatever force is not handled by the tibialis goes directly up to your knee:

Look familiar? Yet no study has ever been done on strengthening this muscle.

The tibialis is the decelerator of your foot, and your foot is your first point of contact, thus:

YOUR TIBIALIS IS YOUR FIRST LINE OF DEFENSE AGAINST BOTH CHRONIC AND ACUTE LOWER BODY INJURIES.

No matter how great I got at the direct knee exercises you will learn as you continue reading, I still suffered from foot pain, Achilles pain, nasty shin splints, and "mystery" lower knee pains.

I recall that at my worst, my foot and lower leg pains were so bad, I would wake up in the morning and wonder, "Will today be a walking-to-the-bathroom morning, or a crawl-to-the-bathroom morning?" Sometimes the pain was too great to bear the load on my feet.

You see, coming from such weak knees, and then jacking up my knee strength so dramatically, I was capable of producing far more force than my lower leg muscles had handled throughout my life. By reverse engineering this situation, I soon realized the tibialis was the missing link in my regimen, and I was overjoyed when I found that transforming this muscle took my knees to the next level of ability!

For example, prior to the Tibialis Raise, I had achieved the ability to dunk, but only when I jumped off two feet. When I did a one-foot jump I got nowhere near as high, and was prone to debilitating foot, shin, and knee pains, which prevented me from trying. Not long after making the Tibialis Raise a standard part of Knee Ability, I was dunking off one foot with ease. All these lower extremity pains disappeared - and never came back.

If you look at your body logically, the Tibialis Raise is a great place to start, regardless of what physical issues you may be having.

STEP 2: THE FHL (FLEXOR HALLUCIS LONGUS) CALF RAISE

The flexor hallucis longus is a powerful muscle which runs all the way from your big toe to your mid-calf. It helps stabilize your ankle when weight is on the ball of your foot, and it's particularly important when force goes through your big toe. Hallucis is a Latin word meaning "of the big toe," so flexor hallucis longus simply means "a long muscle that flexes your big toe."

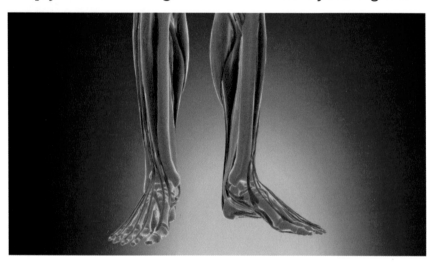

HOW

As soon as you finish your 25 Tibialis Raises, turn around, put your hands against the wall, and back up until your ankles are under enough stretch that your heels come slightly off the ground:

Without bending your knees or hips, raise up until your weight is on your big toes:

If this is too difficult, you can stand closer to the wall, or even use assistance:

Perform 25 reps to the best of your ability, adjusting closer as necessary.

While the Tibialis Raise is likely to be very tough at first, the FHL Calf Raise is more likely to be easy, since the muscles involved are not quite as neglected as the tibialis. To perform one leg at a time, simply wrap the other leg around, which puts even more stretch into the ankle, and more difficulty into the flexor hallucis longus:

If 25 reps with two legs is easy but with one leg is too difficult to perform without a break, simply stop at a number that challenges you, then match that number with your other leg, and return to your original leg, going back and forth until all 25 reps are complete. For example: 10 left leg, 10 right leg, 7 more left leg (total is at 17 now), 7 right leg, 5 left leg (total is at 22), 5 right leg, and finally 3 more each leg for a total of 25 each side.

To re-cap: how far you stand, and whether you use one foot or two, determines difficulty:

WHY

In doing Knee Ability, you're going to be putting stimulus into your legs which may allow you to withstand more force at your knee joint. This is a great thing! However, it means you may unwittingly be putting more force into your feet as a result. For example, let's say you can jump 20 inches high, and after a year of Knee Ability, you can jump 30 inches high. That's awesome, of course, but I don't want you to end up with foot pain, ankle pain, Achilles pain, or shin splints as a byproduct.

Also, your foot itself is the first line of defense for your knees when decelerating, as we saw with the Tibialis Raise, and in the case of the flexor hallucis longus, the same is true when landing:

Whatever force is not absorbed by the ankle, goes into the knee:

Of course we're seeking to improve your KNEE ability, but it makes most sense to also improve the areas which prevent excess knee strain in the first place, and the tibialis and flexor hallucis longus are the first of these areas.

In a traditional calf raise - which I am a fan of, by the way - it is simply not practical to ensure the pressure goes through the big toe. That's why I gravitated to this FHL Calf Raise. I'm sure many coaches throughout history have used similar exercises, but I was never taught anything like it, and I wanted to use a name that would help you understand its purpose.

Also (and this is quite important relative to your knees): the FHL Calf Raise locks in more ankle stretch than a traditional calf raise. For your knees' sake, it is your ankle mobility itself that's a major player, and the FHL Calf Raise is the better tool than a regular calf raise for this job. Just ahead, you'll see how the FHL Calf Raise smoothly progresses you into Step 3:

BUT FIRST, STEP 2B: THE TIBIALIS RAISE... AGAIN!

The Tibialis Raise is so important, you're going to immediately switch back around from the FHL Calf Raise and perform another 25 reps, with the same protocol you did in Step 1.

STEP 3: THE KOT (KNEES OVER TOES) CALF RAISE

The knees over toes calf raise is the first exercise in Knee Ability Zero which directly improves the ability of your knees when they're over your toes. However, it's not actually your knees that will be creating the motion: it is still your ankles that will be lifting you up and down, while your knees will simply hold your pain-free level.

By measurably addressing the ability of your ankles to handle whatever load your knees can, we complete a perfect foundation so that your knee gains result not only in improved knee function, but also in improved foot, ankle, Achilles, and lower leg function! While Knee Ability is most known for creating knee success stories, it also has a multitude of success stories for what lies below!

Let's look at this final progression before directly addressing your knee movements themselves:

HOW

Stand about an arm's length from the wall:

Now gradually reach your knees over your toes to a comfortable level. Ideally, this will be far enough that your heels actually lift slightly off the ground:

It's totally fine if you can't bend your knees much at first, and you're still on the route to success no matter what level you start at, because strength apparently "radiates" about 15 degrees, meaning: If you get strong at one angle, you get strength gains not only at that exact angle, but also at the 15 degrees of bend beyond that! For example, a minimal bend such as this (below) would still be productive:

Don't criticize your current level. Just realize that wherever you fall short now only means you could feel that much better by patiently progressing!

From your pain-free level of knee bend, simply raise your heels up while still keeping your knees over your toes:

Just like FHL Calf Raises, once it's easy to perform 25 consecutive reps with full ankle bend (to the point your heels come slightly off the ground at the bottom), you can begin rebuilding one leg at a time! This puts even more load into your ankle mobility and into the strength of your knee to hold the position:

Like FHL Calf Raises, if 25 in a row with two legs is easy but with one leg is too difficult, simply count your reps on one leg until burnout, then match on the other leg, then switch back to the original leg, and so on until you reach 25 on each side. 25 perfect single-leg reps is your long-term goal.

To recap: how far your knee remains over your toes at bottom *and top* of the exercise, plus whether you are on one leg or two, determines difficulty:

WHY

I got lucky on this exercise and unwittingly solved two problems at once:

Problem 1 was the need for a no-equipment solution for your Achilles. You have two calf muscles: gastrocnemius (think "belly" of the calf) and soleus, which is lower and deeper.

Here's a look beneath the surface to the soleus:

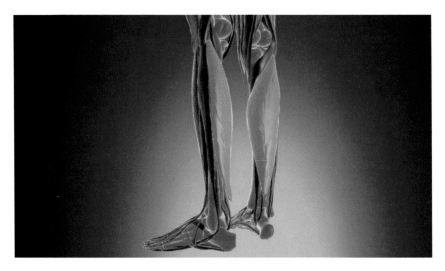

Then notice below how the gastrocnemius overshadows the soleus visually. You have both lateral (toward the outside of your body) and medial (toward the inside of your body) gastrocnemius muscles:

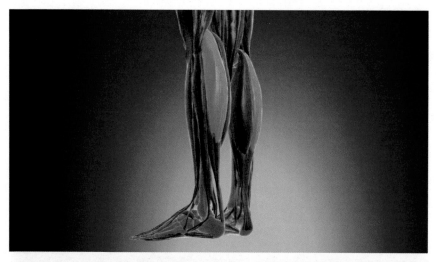

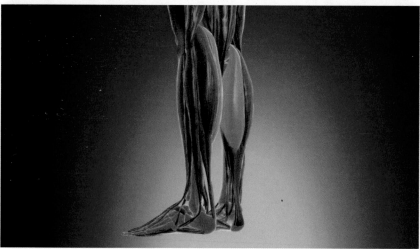

And finally let's look at the Achilles tendon in relation to the Soleus and Gastrocnemius:

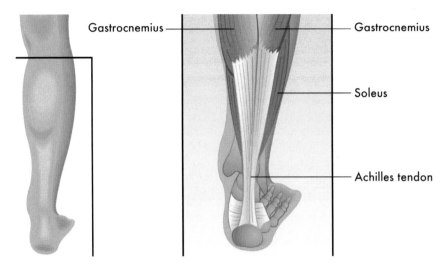

Gastrocnemius — Gastrocnemius

— Soleus

— Achilles tendon

Your Achilles tendon looks pretty big, huh? Yep: It's the biggest tendon in your body! It is a very interesting phenomenon when you realize that as your muscles get smaller, your tendons get bigger. For example, your glutes are huge compared to your calves, but your gluteal tendons are small compared to your Achilles!

Thus: Your hips are your biggest source of power, while your ankles are your biggest source of springs. The knees are left in the middle - a perfect balance of both springs and power (or PAIN, as they are subject to ramifications from both your ankles and your hips - ouch!).

Your soleus is more directly related to your Achilles health than your gastroc is, but your soleus isn't worked as much as your gastroc in a traditional standing calf raise. Fortunately, a bent-knee calf raise prioritizes your soleus and handles this issue.

For this reason, my gym used to be full of seated calf machines. Your gym has a row of bench presses; mine had a row of seated calf machines!

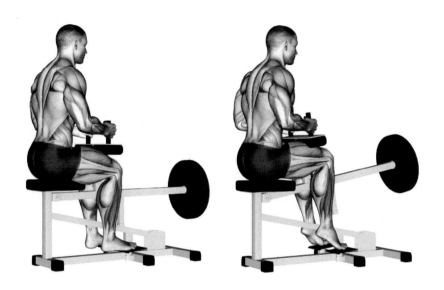

Before long my gym was overrun. I was working from 4 a.m. to midnight, seven days a week, with no days off for multiple years in a row. More people needed my help than I was capable of handling in person, so I decided to become an online coach and take more responsibility.

I quickly ran into the problem of what to do if your gym doesn't have a seated calf machine, and through much trial and error, the KOT Calf Raise was born. Little did I know at the time, I had also solved the bridge between ankle exercises and knee exercises!

In Step 4, you will directly address your knees, and in most cases this works just fine. However, the KOT Calf Raise already starts putting money in the bank toward your knee ability, so your progress will be smoother. In very sensitive cases, we have an option that strengthens the knees without even risking any painful movement, since you can monitor exactly how far you reach your toes.

Before we go on, you should know that your body relies heavily on your ability in the KOT Calf Raise when putting all your weight on your leg to push off in a sprint, as well as in the rear leg just before jump takeoff, and again upon landing:

Many Achilles and knee injuries happen in these actions, and the KOT Calf Raise works against these odds!

STEP 4: THE PATRICK STEP

The farther and stronger your knees can go over your toes, the more protected you are - but how do you get there? The Patrick Step provides a safe and measurable route to put energy into this ability without ever needing to work through pain in the process!

HOW

Start with balance and/or assistance. A wall is great for balance, and PVC pipes are great for assistance, too:

Now reach the inside foot forward, and slowly lower the heel to the floor:

Pause fully to ensure you don't bounce in order to get momentum, then raise back up:

Understand you are fully in control of how much you work your knee over your toes by how far you reach the inside heel:

Notice how the farther you reach, the more your knee has to bend! Your end goal is actually to go until your ankle cannot bend anymore without letting your inside heel touch the floor, thus requiring your knee to support your full weight, to full ankle bend:

Being able to perform 25 consecutive reps to full ankle bend helps prepare for the fifth movement of Knee Ability Zero, but there's no rush to get to this level, and it's very important to never, ever work through pain. Know the following rule:

PAIN = DESTRUCTION

Your body uses pain to communicate to you, and by acknowledging this two-way communication you can actually handle the source of your pain rather than just trying to "shut up" what your body is saying to you. We'll go into more detail on this in a later section of the book which addresses the following things, but realize that ice, painkillers, etc., are examples of your knee trying to talk to you, and you saying, "Shut up, Knee!" If someone in real life has a problem with you and you tell them to shut up, it may handle the problem temporarily but has a higher likelihood of coming back to be an even bigger problem. Your knees are no different!

On the other hand, if you feel burning in your muscles on this exercise, rather than pain inside the joint, you're stimulating greater protection for your knee, giving us the following counter-rule:

PAIN-FREE MUSCULAR BURN = CONSTRUCTION

To recap: How far you reach, how much you assist your strength, how much you assist your balance, and whether you touch your heel to the floor or keep it free-floating, all together determine difficulty:

WHY

With the Patrick Step, we have a scalable way for you to put energy on your ability with your knees over your toes without ever working through pain.

In a perfect world, that's all the data you would need to succeed with this exercise, but in reality, most people have an imbalance between sides, meaning one side feels better than the other side.

To remedy this you'll start and finish on your more difficult side. This way you get two sets on your weak side and one set on your strong side.

It's not only weakness but also *imbalance* that increases our likelihood of pain and injury. If one leg has greater abilities than the other leg, you are more likely to wind up in excessive situations *not just for the weaker leg* but also for the stronger side trying to help out beyond its intended duties.

Don't worry, though, if you have an imbalance. Rather, look at this situation optimistically. Whatever you feel like now, you'll feel that much better once you're balanced, while getting even more athletic as a result! And this "start and finish on the weak side" strategy consistently creates balance between sides!

ALTERNATIVE STEP 4: THE PATRICK STEP *UP*

While not technically "zero" - this is as close to zero as it gets.

With a 6-inch (15 centimeter) cinder block for just a few bucks from your local home improvement store, you can get a precise measurement of ability.

6 inches is the highest I advise, and you could get creative about reducing that height via lower steps ("aerobic steps" are found in almost all commercial gyms) or use of a solid object on the floor. You'll notice Alissa using a PVC pipe to show how not only the range, but also the strength, regresses to virtually any level:

Now let's look at my feet. By stepping my front heel in front of my working toes, I create a solid measurement of ability:

25 reps per side in the Patrick Step *Up* may be done as an alternative to the Patrick Step. If you have a more difficult side, I would coach you to start with 25 reps on that side, then match those 25 reps on the better side, then do another 25 reps on the more difficult side. I've seen in myself and others, over and over, that you are *not* destined to a "bad side" the rest of your life. Your potential to even out is much greater than you might think, even for some of the most gnarly knee injuries and surgeries!

These regressions are how I got my own knees out of the muck. If these regressions worked so well for getting me out of pain and returning the gift of basketball to me, why would I go back to traditional training? Instead, I have not deviated from the exact principles that saved me. For example, Step 4 of "Advanced" Zero is still the Patrick Step Up, just allowing weights. However, that's only done once a week, whereas the bodyweight version in Zero is allowed more often. Greater loads and demands require greater recovery.

My greatest contributions to the field of exercise are not extreme methods. Rather, they are:

1. *Scalable* routes so the fragile can become less fragile, if not bulletproof compared to the norm, *without* ever increasing risk or pain in the process.

2. The *marriage* of exercise and bulletproofing, meaning: "Rehab" and "exercise" do not have to be two separate categories. In fact, by turning effective rehab methods into exercise, we open the door to higher levels of athleticism and quality of life as we age.

A very special thanks goes to my wife, Alissa, for this entire category of Step 4. Reverse step ups have been used for decades to salvage sports careers and win gold medals, but the popular forms of reverse step ups involve more complexity and difficulty. The reverse step up pioneers were Carl Petersen (Canadian downhill ski physiotherapist) and Charles Poliquin (arguably the most Olympic medal-producing strength coach of all time). In my programming system of "Zero" then "Dense" then "Standards," I use the Patrick Step

Up in Zero, the Poliquin Step Up in Dense, and the Petersen Step Up in Standards.

Alissa instinctively insisted on this simpler reverse step up, and I eventually realized the full power of regression and *patiently* building a whole new beast, rather than rushing to the end goal.

Only the Poliquin and Petersen versions were commonly known and used, and even those were pretty obscure. So I guess we should all thank Alissa as the third reverse step up pioneer, who has now made the entire subject of reverse step ups approachable and understood as a potentially life-changing method which scales to *any* level.

Just yesterday I received a text message from an NFL player telling me that his entire team does "the Patrick Step Up" every week. It's still up to the strength coaches of that team to correctly coach the form and fully understand the following...

Your knee tendons recover slower than your muscles, and your knee ligaments recover even slower than your knee tendons!

These are facts about muscles, tendons, and ligaments - not my opinions.

But tendons and ligaments *do* have the potential to grow and strengthen the same way muscles do!

So by the very nature of those facts, you can see how your knee potential is actually *huge* - *if* we respect that process by training at our pain-free level and then by *continuing* that process even after we are "out of pain" rather than reverting back to our same old training and discarding or stopping progress on what got us out of pain.

STEP 5: THE ATG (ASS TO GRASS) SPLIT SQUAT

This is my personal favorite exercise, because I know if I did only this one exercise for the rest of my life, I'd still live in the upper 1% of knee ability.

Everything you've done to this point helps prepare your ankles and knees for the ATG Split Squat, but an added factor of hip flexor length enters the equation, so first understand that while I want you to eventually be able to perform this exercise on flat ground, you may have to initially use a step. Notice the difference in hip flexibility:

(More hip flexor length)

(Less hip flexor length)

With continued Patrick Step to be able to handle your full weight, plus front foot elevation to compensate for flexibility limitation, the majority of people I've coached have successfully gotten into this exercise without pain. However, there's still one final option for regression, which is using something for assistance:

If front foot elevation plus assistance still doesn't allow you to get into this exercise pain-free, it is simply too much, too soon. Continued work on the previous four exercises, plus the exercises after this step, have gotten trainees there in relatively short time.

HOW

The first step - no pun intended - is establishing how long your step is. People have varying leg lengths and varying degrees of flexibility - fortunately, this isn't something I have ever found the need to measure. You simply play with your foot distance until you have perfect form, and eventually it won't take any thinking about.

Too close of a step does not allow enough depth, and thus prevents full coverage:

While too long of a step does not allow enough knee over toes, and thus prevents full coverage:

The correct step distance allows the front hamstring to fully cover the calf, with perfectly upright torso:

With back toes still pressed - NOT rolling over,

(Correct)

(Incorrect)

And with back knee NOT touching the floor.

Lower down slowly, fully pause in the bottom position, rise back up without altering posture, and repeat!

Perform 5 sets of 5 reps per side, back and forth, taking up to 30 seconds between sides if you feel you need a break. Just like with Step 4, you'll apply the "start and finish on the more difficult side" if you have one. Thus, 6 sets on the weak, 5 sets on the strong.

When 5 sets of 5 reps per side with 30-second breaks is easy, your next goal is:

3 sets of 8 with 40-second breaks, starting and finishing with a 4th set on the weaker side if you have one. This results in more done in less time. When that's easy, your next goal is:

2 sets of 12 with 50-second breaks, starting and finishing with a third set on the weaker side if you have one. This results in even more work done in less time. And when that's easy, your final goal in this program is:

1 set of 25 per side with a 60-second break. But even at this level, if one side doesn't feel as good as the other, you would start on the tougher side and finish on the tougher side, ie: 2 sets weak, 1 set strong. This has perhaps the most powerful effects I've seen on truly correcting imbalances in your ankles, knees, and hips!

To recap: how much you elevate your front foot and how much assistance you use determine difficulty:

WHY

When you stop fully bending your knees, your body stops sending synovial fluid which lubricates and brings nutrients to your joints. That's because your body thinks you're no longer using them.

But forcing your knees to bend through pain is also not the answer!

When you have a problem, forcing the issue can create a short-term disaster.

On the other hand, avoiding a problem completely can create a long-term disaster!

In a perfect world, we would just never lose that innate childhood ability to fully bend our knees. For those of us who have lost that ability, the ATG Split Squat is a patient but remarkably effective solution...

In the real world, the overwhelming majority of us have imbalanced legs and knees and thus receive negative ramifications from bilateral (two legs) squats. Any difference between sides manifests when you squat with two legs, leaving the weaker knee vulnerable, or worse: causing you to favor the stronger knee, and thus making the imbalance even worse! Enter: the ATG Split Squat.

In addition to being perhaps *the* most critical exercise which rebuilt my knees, the ATG Split Squat also fixed my tight hip flexors.

The tighter our hip flexors, the more pulled forward we get. The modern lifestyle of excessive sitting doesn't help. Bilateral squats don't fix this, whereas ATG Split Squats do!

Once you can get into good, flat ground ATG Split Squats, you're ahead of the game and have a chance to stay out of the trap forever! I advise getting this ability and never losing it!

My beautiful mother is 67 years young and can run, squat, etc., without pain. A few years ago she had debilitating chronic hip pain, then she started the ATG Split Squat with front foot elevated and assistance, and now she's pain-free and can do flat ground!

(Even Momma better have perfect form.)

I've personally done over 10,000 ATG Split Squats, and I've now coached over 10,000 ATG Split Squats in-person and online. It is the gift that keeps on giving.

At this point, we've paved a route for amazing ability in our knees...

...and with pain-free knees, anti-gravity and bulletproofing goals become so much easier to achieve...

...but our training session doesn't end here!

STEP 6: ELEPHANT WALK

This is the first of the "accessory" exercises in the Knee Ability Zero formula. Everything we've done to this point directly contributes to you being able to handle more force through your leg muscles, but you can only use the muscles that extend your knee (the quads) to the degree that the muscles which flex the knee (the hamstrings) can stretch:

HOW

The test of adequately flexible hamstrings is the ability to have your palms on the floor without bending your knees:

If this position looks tough, remember that my nickname used to be "Old Man," and at the worst of my knee problems, my toes looked like they were a mile away!

By starting with your hands farther out (you can even lift up on your fingertips, or use a box or step to elevate), with knees bent, and then extending one leg at a time, you can get twice the load of a regular hamstring stretch:

(Farther out, on fingertips)

(You could even lift up with a box, step, etc.)

(Extend one leg)

(Bend again)

(Extend the other leg)

When you can comfortably extend each leg, you can back up farther. Over time, this will continue all the way until your palms are on the floor, in front of your toes:

Perform 30 reps per side, being sure to keep breathing throughout the set.

And to recap: this exercise can scale as simply as elevating your hands!

WHY

Once a foundation of Knee Ability Zero is laid, I then gradually add equipment and load in my further programs. This includes training your hamstring strength in a variety of ways. A palms-to-floor Elephant Walk, or moving your way closer to it, helps ensure that your hamstrings will have a nice balance of flexibility when we start addressing their strength.

STEP 7: L-SIT

With greater leg power comes greater responsibility! No matter how strong your legs are, you still have to pick them back up when you walk, run, etc:

Your hip flexors aren't prominent "mirror-muscles," so they've lost much of the attention to the "6-pack:"

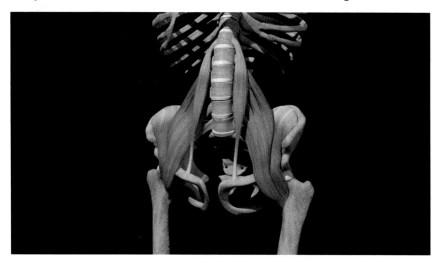

As you can see, the hip flexors are made up of a number of smaller muscles attached from the spine itself (your hip flexors are linked closely to lower back pain!) and extending all the way down your mid-thigh.

Interestingly, the hip flexors have more strength potential than your abs, and since they work along with your abs, they might just be the weak link that's holding back your core potential! I don't do any traditional "core" exercises, and my abs are getting by alright. I'm a pale guy but with a good photographer, my 6-pack ain't half bad...

In my style of training, the goal is not to "neglect" your abs, but rather to train them "from the ground up" by using your feet as the source of load, ensuring your hip flexors never lag behind!

HOW

The measure of your hip flexors being up to par is simple: Can you hold your body off the ground?

There are three levels of progression to this point:

Level 1 is just holding one leg off the ground at a time, for a two-count:

Leaning back reduces difficulty:

Leaning forward increases difficulty:

Set a timer and go back and forth for 60 seconds.

Level 2 is the same drill, but holding your butt off the floor as well! Also for 60 seconds:

When you go back and forth for 60 seconds with your butt off the floor, you can probably do Level 3: a full L-Sit!

At this point you're in the upper 1% of humans, but you could go even further by setting a timer and seeing how long you can hold. Holding for 20 seconds straight is the goal in my system, but I would not stop you from holding even longer!

Now to clarify exactly how you would do your sets, let's break down two distinct levels:

1. I recommend setting a 60-second timer and performing Levels 1 and 2, holding one foot up for a two-count, switch, repeat. You can start with Level 2 and if that taps out, regress right down to Level 1 mid-set. When you can do Level 2 for 60 seconds, you can probably do Level 3 for at least a few seconds...

2. Once working on Level 3, you would simply count "one... two... three..." until tap-out. Rest for about 10 seconds. Then continue "four... five..." until you have counted 20 seconds. 20 seconds straight is exceptional and I think is plenty for most sports goals.

Like most exercises of Knee Ability Zero, I suggest doing one set every other day to ensure fullest recovery.

Final note: I grew up in fear of strengthening my hip-flexors. Multiple trainers told me that strengthening my hip-flexors would cause them to tighten up. But the ATG Split Squat solves this by strengthening the hip-flexors through a *stretched* position. The various trainers who steered me away from strengthening my hip-flexors didn't have anywhere near the hip-flexor flexibility that I have now! At the time, my hip-flexors were both weak *and* stiff. The solution was to train their strength in shortened (L-Sit) and lengthened (ATG Split Squat) positions. This strategy consistently applied with perfect form has now broken flexibility and athleticism barriers for thousands of people.

To re-cap, the exercise really just scales as simply as: how much of your feet and butt are off the ground?

WHY

Let's break this down into 3 reasons, since each is quite different:

1. In relation to your knees, we know there's success waiting for us by addressing the muscles which function to withstand force at your ankle and knee joints, but we also know that in doing so, we may experience some degree of muscle growth in these areas. I have never observed this to be excessively heavy, but this is weight that must be accounted for. If I'm going to make your ankles and knees stronger, I must make your hip flexors stronger so that your legs feel just as light, if not lighter, and are not subject to hip flexor strains due to imbalance. This brings us to point number 2:

2. The hip flexors are the biggest difference between regular humans and elite sprinters. There is no doubt many of my clients want to run faster: from competitive distance runners to NFL players with millions of dollars on the line based on their speed, to dads who just want to be able to enjoy sports with their kids without tweaking something. For me personally, even after I had the leg power to dunk, I still lacked top-end speed, meaning: I had powerful explosion, but once I built up to my fastest, I couldn't hold onto it for very long, I lacked the last gear needed to be as fast as the pro basketball and football players I was training.

Fast-forward a couple years of hip flexor training and my speed is now on par with the average NFL defensive back! In high school I famously ran a 6-

second 40-yard dash. My coach thought his stopwatch was malfunctioning, and he made me run it again. After a second 6-second time, he made me take off my shoes to prove I didn't have weights in them. For the record, I really like this coach, but I think he was in shock and didn't know how to handle a 6-second 40. My lack of speed tormented me for years, and one of my worst fears in life was a footrace, but not anymore! Now, my speed on the basketball court is one of my greatest strengths, and I look back just amazed that out of the dozens of trainers I went to, no one ever made me confront my weak hip flexors. Sadly for naturally slow athletes like me, avoidance of strengthening the hip-flexors became a popular opinion due to lack of a solution for lengthening them with the ATG Split Squat.

Here's me at age 16...

Start of a fastbreak, right?

Think again!

I was simply slower than everyone else on the court. Now when I play, my speed is my greatest weapon! And thanks to Knee Ability, I can run and jump as hard as I want without thinking about my knees.

3. Lastly, I think of stronger hip flexors as long-term knee bulletproofers because they lead to less wear and tear over the course of seasons, years, and life. When your hip flexors are weak, you have to thud harder along the ground to get from point A to B than your body was naturally designed to do. Squats, deadlifts, etc., train the ability of your hips to extend, but the fastest guys I've trained also have elite hip flexor strength. Since hip-flexor strength isn't a commonly taught and measurable thing, like squats and deadlifts are, I've encountered countless athletes who are still slow despite getting as "strong" as the fast guys. Fortunately, as the hip-flexors and other key speed areas come up, I've seen over and over again that these slow athletes can be fast, because: If you

can get strong in one area, you can get strong in another!

Conclusion: Hip extensors (glutes and hamstrings!) are sexy and powerful, but hip flexors are often the reason that hard-working athletes remain slow, and you're adding unnecessary long-term pain and injury to your feet, ankles, Achilles, shins, and knees to the degree that your hip flexor-to-extensor ratio is busted.

Do we want strong hip extensors? Yep!

Do we want strong hip flexors? Yep!

This ain't rocket science, but it IS science. You must confront the biology of your knees and the rest of your body if you want to maximize not only your genetic potential for anti-gravity and bulletproofing, but also your quality of life for the long haul.

If you rely on where exercise science has put its money, you're subject to its errors. It doesn't matter what the findings are if it's not looking fairly and accurately to begin with!

We are still human. We are still fragile. Every day, though, we're seeing life-changing wins become the norm just by training according to physics and biology through the methods in this book. Something *can* be done about soaring pain and injury statistics.

STEP 8: COUCH STRETCH

For knee tendon freedom, I highly advise achieving and maintaining the ability to have your shin and shoulders against a wall:

HOW

For some, the ankle itself may be too tight to start against a wall, but a chair's lower seat allows you to begin. This appears to be the reason for the name "Couch" Stretch:

Always use thick padding under the knee. You may be more comfortable with even more than I'm using in the picture. When in doubt... MORE PADDING!

When this gets easy, you can gradually work against the wall as follows:

1) Start sideways in order to easily have your knee close to the wall:

2) Then spin around and lean forward so you can easily slide your back foot up the wall:

3) From here, you can work your hands up your front thigh and then to your hips, thus increasing the stretch (as you are able to comfortably):

4) Your long-term goal is shoulders to wall, and from there, I want you to get comfortable actually contracting the glute on that side:

Perform 60 seconds per side, being sure to work only at a level where you can relax and breathe without pain.

WHY

When the quads and hip flexors are tight, they pull the kneecap upward, making you more likely to experience pain in the patellar tendon below:

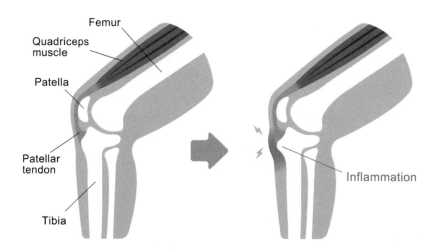

Femur

Quadriceps
muscle

Patella

Patellar
tendon

Tibia

Inflammation

Also, your quads and hip-flexors are the direct opposing muscles to your hamstrings and glutes, which you rely on heavily when you sprint and jump...

It's also worth reminding you that your ATG Split Squats a) improve your hip flexor length, and b) improve your quad strength - so the better you get at the ATG Split Squat, the more comfortable and fruitful your Couch Stretch efforts will be.

Strength and flexibility adaptation take time, so acknowledge yourself for every 1% you get better. You'll soon find yourself waking up to a different reality without ever working through pain in the process.

That marks the end of the Knee Ability Zero formula!

RECAP

3 times per week:

Step 1: Tibialis Raise: 25 reps

Step 2: FHL Calf Raise: 25 reps

Step 2B: Tibialis Raise (again): 25 reps

Step 3: KOT Calf Raise: 25 reps

Step 4: Patrick Step: 25 reps, but you can perform an extra set if you have a weaker side, until balanced

Step 5: ATG Split Squat: 5 sets of 5 reps per side with 30-second breaks between each (and progressing to 25 straight reps per the guide in its section)

Step 6: Elephant Walk: 30 reps per side

Step 7: L-Sit: 60 seconds

Step 8: Couch Stretch: 60 seconds per side

That marks the end of this book - almost!

Thank you so much for reading.

FINAL WORDS FROM THE 12-YEAR-OLD ME WITH KNEE PAIN

I never intended to publish this book.

Until now, my entire business has consisted only of obsessively coaching perfect form.

I owned a gym for 7 years and my attention to detail on form-coaching was in a different universe.

I am the guy on hands and knees literally guiding your body in the ATG Split Squat, *never* being OK with working through pain, always massaging every possible nuance of regression, even innovating methods of troubleshooting that have never been done before, all to ensure that you're able to enjoy each exercise without pain, and make *progress*.

In 2018 I was helping a friend who had moved away. He would send me his last set on each unorthodox exercise, and I would coach his form.

He told me I should take my program online.

To perform this exact service online, I wasn't able to get any business advisor to believe in charging less than $99 per month. Even my parents thought I would have to charge at least $99 per month for that level of service.

I got everyone to agree to a half-price discount for initial sign-ups, and I never went back!

12-year-old me with knee pain probably would not have paid $99 a month online.

12-year-old me with knee pain might have paid $49.50/month.

From age 12 on, I never stopped working. I had my first job at 12, doing clerical work at a chiropractor's office and being paid as "utilities."

From there, I was always mowing lawns, washing cars, painting walls.

I was always able to afford investing in human bulletproofing research, programs and equipment because I always worked.

But some people may have to do extra work just to make ends meet.

So I took things even further and made the first month of my online membership half price again - $24.75 - with no long-term contract and no data held back. Meaning: for $24.75, a 12-year-old me with knee pain could sign up and learn everything I now know about training, including every program in my system.

A 12-year-old me with knee pain in a single month would have read every article and watched every video and memorized every program.

But one morning last week I woke up and realized that a 12-year-old me with knee pain would have been even more likely to buy a physical book on Amazon. My aunt even gave me Amazon gift cards every year back then! "Oh NO! BOOKS?" But back then there was no book giving me a knee program to change my life.

Now there is.

And the decision was really that simple.

In fact, the go-to business rule that has served me best is asking myself this question: "What would the 12-year-old me with knee pain have wanted?"

Just know that by studying my or *any* system of exercise, the best coaches I've talked to share the same common denominators above all else: patient mastery of *form*, scalable progressions, and not working through pain. That way you can thrive the rest of your life and reach vistas much greater than anything you could achieve in the short-term!

And if you plan on helping *others* with the data, every inaccuracy in your own form could then manifest as mistakes in those you help.

On the other hand, the ripple effect of perfect form has been even greater in those I've coached.

I read every success story that comes in, and I now count more success stories per day created by my membership helping *others* than by me helping my members!

My personal count as of today is 2,299 knee success stories, among thousands more for the rest of the body, but that doesn't count what my members are creating to help others, which is quickly surpassing my own count.

That's the only way we will reverse worldwide statistics of knee suffering which have not stopped climbing for decades.

My online programs are all body strength and mobility programs, with your form coached on all key exercises, plus questions answered, on average, in less than 2 hours - 7 days a week. We have our own web coding team and we simply never stop trying to get better.

For those who give my membership a shot, I hope it's among the greatest values for your dollar of anything you've ever bought.

Yours in Bulletproofing,

Ben

Made in United States
Orlando, FL
13 October 2022

23261390R00055